Birth

Date

Day

Time

Place

Weight

Early Or late?

The wOrld when I was bOrned

AbOut my parents

and grandparents

and eXtended family

sisters and brOthers?

Family scandal, Suspicions, rumours...

...Or skeletons in the closet

Age 0-10, my hOme memOries

and Family traditions

School days

Best subjects

_____

_____

_____

Worst Subjects

_____

_____

_____

Exam results

_____

_____

_____

Teachers

_____

_____

_____

Punishments

school dinners

.

Reports

Early ambitions

The age I left

the Teenage years

being a Student

Subject(S)

_____

_____

_____

_____

_____

_____

_____

_____

_____

_____

_____

_____

_____

_____

_____

_____

_____

_____

_____

Stupid things I've done
(bollard stealing incidents)

Qualifications

the Opposite seX?

first interest

_____
_____
_____
_____
_____
_____
_____
_____

first kiss

_____
_____
_____
_____
_____

first date

my Friends

Graduating and/or first jObs

My twenties

HObbies deVelopment

Pets

a few favourites

Drink

Food

Pub

Sport

Colour

Clothes

Bands

Best gig

Film

Club

SOme holidays

MY thirties

MOre abOut
the Opposite sex...

_____

_____

_____

_____

_____

_____

_____

_____

The One that gOt away?

_____

_____

_____

_____

Partners, marriage, kids...?

my Career path

Best and Worst JObs

My Travels

My view of the World

Other cultures

Politics

Religion

SOciety

my Own family

bringing Up Kids

My forties

my Marriage(s)

cars I've Owned

things I've Learned

Places I've lived

Sorries I'd like to say

_____

_____

_____

_____

_____

_____

Thank yous I owe

_____

_____

_____

_____

_____

_____

_____

_____

People I'll never forget

Claims to fame?

Big influences in my life

my Fifties

My health

mOre FavouRites

Country

City

BOok

Film

FoOd

Restaurant

SpOrt

ARtist

MUsic

Car

COmedian

Actor

Charity

Colour

Smell

Feeling

Season

Time of day

Weather

Biscuit

Clothing

Wine

Beer

Tea/Coffee

Quote

my Sixties

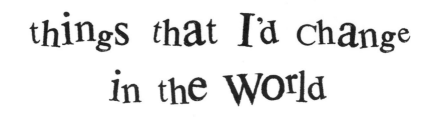

things that I'd change in the World

what I cOuld have dOne Better

Secrets I've kept

my 3 wishes

my 70s, 80s, 90s

if...

If you could relive one year of your life, which would it be and why?

If you could rescue one object from a fire, what would it be?

If you could change something about your physical appearance, what would it be?

If a film was made about your life, which actor would play you?

If someone were to sing a song about you and your life, what would it be?

---

biggest JOy in life

biggest Regret

My letter to the world

_____
_____
_____
_____
_____
_____
_____
_____
_____
_____
_____
_____

Famous last Words

_____
_____
_____
_____